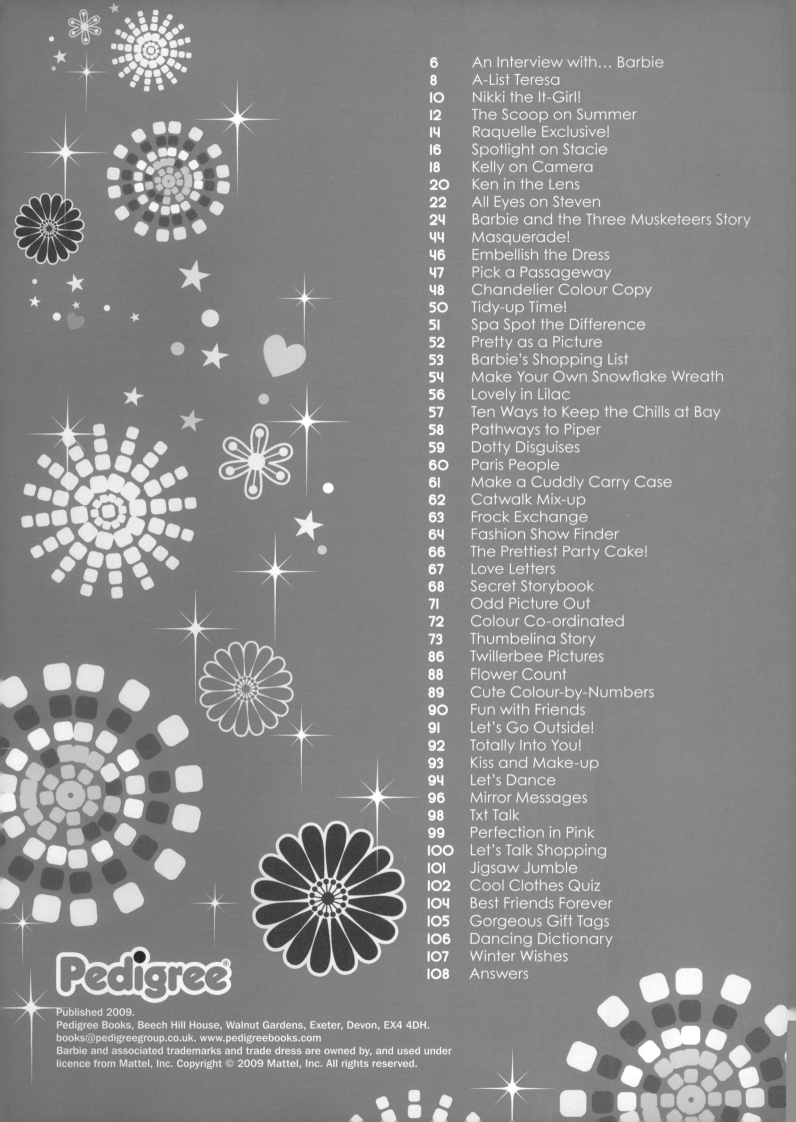

6	An Interview with… Barbie
8	A-List Teresa
10	Nikki the It-Girl!
12	The Scoop on Summer
14	Raquelle Exclusive!
16	Spotlight on Stacie
18	Kelly on Camera
20	Ken in the Lens
22	All Eyes on Steven
24	Barbie and the Three Musketeers Story
44	Masquerade!
46	Embellish the Dress
47	Pick a Passageway
48	Chandelier Colour Copy
50	Tidy-up Time!
51	Spa Spot the Difference
52	Pretty as a Picture
53	Barbie's Shopping List
54	Make Your Own Snowflake Wreath
56	Lovely in Lilac
57	Ten Ways to Keep the Chills at Bay
58	Pathways to Piper
59	Dotty Disguises
60	Paris People
61	Make a Cuddly Carry Case
62	Catwalk Mix-up
63	Frock Exchange
64	Fashion Show Finder
66	The Prettiest Party Cake!
67	Love Letters
68	Secret Storybook
71	Odd Picture Out
72	Colour Co-ordinated
73	Thumbelina Story
86	Twillerbee Pictures
88	Flower Count
89	Cute Colour-by-Numbers
90	Fun with Friends
91	Let's Go Outside!
92	Totally Into You!
93	Kiss and Make-up
94	Let's Dance
96	Mirror Messages
98	Txt Talk
99	Perfection in Pink
100	Let's Talk Shopping
101	Jigsaw Jumble
102	Cool Clothes Quiz
104	Best Friends Forever
105	Gorgeous Gift Tags
106	Dancing Dictionary
107	Winter Wishes
108	Answers

Published 2009.
Pedigree Books, Beech Hill House, Walnut Gardens, Exeter, Devon, EX4 4DH.
books@pedigreegroup.co.uk. www.pedigreebooks.com

Barbie ™

My new annual has been written especially for you! Inside you'll find fairytales, fashion tips plus a treasure trove of puzzles and games. Now there's no need to get the blues in the cold winter weather! Grab a hot chocolate, curl up and enjoy...

Barbie xx

£7.99

An Interview with...
BARBIE

In these pages you'll find an exclusive interview with me, plus all the people who make my world so special. We've got together to share our secrets, hopes and dreams, as well as posing for some glamorous new photos!

So this is me! I'm an actress who also loves to sing and dance. When I'm not performing or studying at school, my favourite times are spent hanging out with my amazing friends. I'm crazy about animals and dancing and I also have a passion for fashion!

Height:
170 cm

Eyes:
Sky blue

Hair:
Golden blonde

Best friend:
Teresa

Favourite colour:
Pink

Biggest talents:
Acting and singing.

Pets:
Golden retriever Taffy
Piper the Westie
Cat Mika
Horse Tawney

Top hobby:
Playing with Nikki and Teresa in my band, Barbie and the Rockers.

Favourite motto:
Dream big and you can do anything.

Ideal Christmas present:
A pretty diary ready to be filled with a year's worth of new adventures!

The cause that's closest to my heart:
Making sure that animals everywhere are loved and looked after.

Chilling with Taffy

Working the red carpet!

Another day on set

Barbie X

A-list Teresa

Teresa is the kindest companion that any girl could wish for! She is a sweet and thoughtful person who brings out the best in everybody. Even though she's a busy superstar, Teresa always has time for her pals.

Height:
170 cm

Eyes:
Warm brown

Hair:
Brunette

Best friend:
Barbie

Favourite colour:
Lilac

Biggest talents:
Acting and singing.

Top hobby:
Sketching and drawing. Teresa is a talented artist!

Favourite motto:
Friends are forever.

Ideal Christmas present:
A pretty new tutu to wear to her ballet class.

The cause that's closest to my heart:
Protecting the world's most beautiful places, so that they will always there be to shared.

Performing at the ballet school review

Striking a pose

Me and my study buddy!

Teresa X

Nikki the It-Girl!

Nikki is not just funny, bubbly and outgoing, she's a total fashionista too! This sassy girlfriend is not afraid to speak her mind– when I want an honest opinion I always know that I can count on Nikki to tell it like it is.

Height:
170 cm

Eyes:
Deep brown

Hair:
Black

Best friends:
Barbie and Teresa

Favourite colour:
Blue

Biggest talent:
Dancing.

Top hobby:
Customising clothes. Nikki can rustle up a daring new outfit in minutes!

Favourite motto:
Never take no for answer.

Ideal Christmas present:
The latest new It-bag, preferably in every colour!

The cause that's closest to my heart:
Standing up to bullies.

All dressed up for a celebrity appearance

Born to shop

Some well-earned time off!

Nikki X

The Scoop on Summer

Summer is an inspiration to me! She's a brilliant tennis champ who never lets life pass her by. Summer has an adventurous spirit and a love of the great outdoors. She's just the person to make me smile if I'm ever feeling down!

Height:
170 cm

Eyes:
Hazy green

Hair:
Strawberry blonde

Best friend:
Teresa

Favourite colour:
Orange

Biggest talent:
Playing tennis.

Top hobby:
High-energy sports such as rock climbing and wind-surfing.

Favourite motto:
Today I'll be faster, stronger, better.

Ideal Christmas present:
A rucksack printed with a bright happy pattern!

The cause that's closest to my heart:
Summer is proud to be green. She always tries to respect the environment.

A star on the court

Another day, another work out

Guest of honour at a Midsummer ball

Summer X

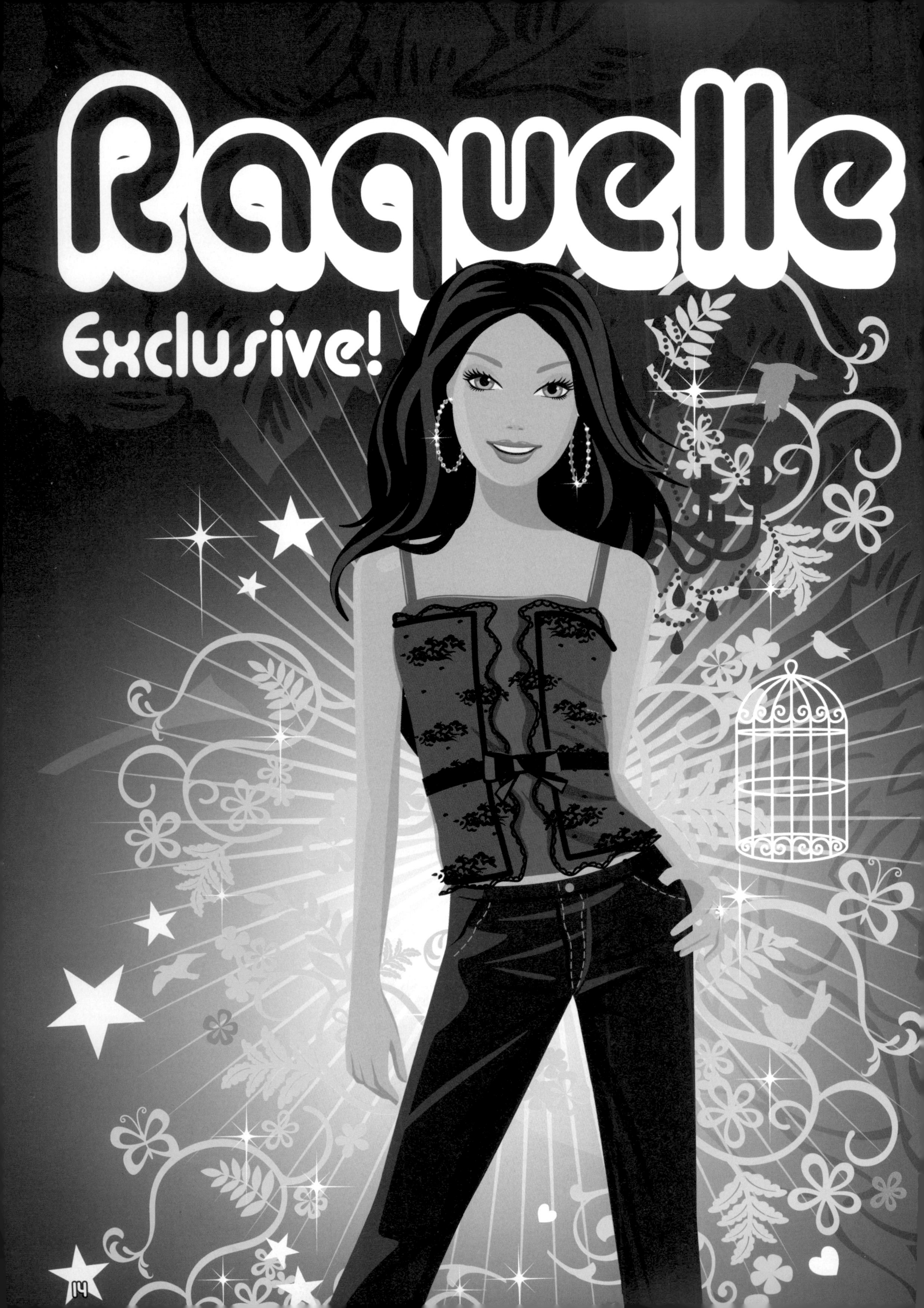
Raquelle
Exclusive!

No wonder everybody's talking about Raquelle! This camera-loving trendsetter can always be seen in the hottest new clothes. Raquelle is a supermodel who's not so keen on sharing the spotlight, but she's also a loyal and true friend.

Height:
170 cm

Eyes:
Sapphire blue

Hair:
Black

Best friend:
Nikki

Favourite colour:
Purple

Biggest talents:
Modelling and acting.

Top hobby:
Shopping, shopping and more shopping.

Favourite motto:
Let's talk about me!

Ideal Christmas present:
Anything designer, especially if it's studded with diamanté.

The cause that's closest to my heart:
Raquelle's jet set lifestyle doesn't leave much time for campaigning. If her friends are fighting for a cause however, she'll always throw her weight behind them.

Behind the camera for a change

Absolutely flawless

Attending an award ceremony

Raquelle X

Spotlight on Stacie

My sister Stacie is a total cutie! She's a shy person with a big heart and a wonderful sense of humour. On the weekend I like to escape the cameras and relax with my little sis – we spend hours giggling and sharing stories!

Height:
137 cm

Eyes:
Sky blue

Hair:
Dark blonde

Favourite colour:
Pink

Biggest talent:
Playing the piano, although Stacie doesn't like to have an audience.

Top hobby:
Painting, drawing and junk modelling.

Favourite motto:
Everyone should dare to dream.

Ideal Christmas present:
An artbox crammed full of sequins, coloured paper and stick-on shapes.

The cause that's closest to my heart:
Stacie always puts her hand up to support her school fund-raising events.

Sisters in the sunshine!

Creating another masterpiece

Stacie X

kelly on camera

Kelly has only just started school, but she's a superstar already. My baby sister has performed in heaps of movies with me, stealing the show every single time! There's no doubt about it, Kelly is a bubbly bundle of fun!

Height:
107 cm

Eyes:
Sky blue

Hair:
Sunny blonde

Favourite colour:
Peach

Biggest talents:
Acting and singing.

Top hobby:
Standing in front of her bedroom mirror, working out new dance routines.

Favourite motto:
I can do it too!

Ideal Christmas present:
A big dressing-up box full of my old party clothes!

The cause that's closest to my heart:
Kelly loves her playmates. She'll try and help anyone in trouble, no matter how big the problem might be.

Kelly always makes a splash!

Red carpet kid

Kelly X

Ken is an all-round good guy. My friends and I love hanging out with him after school – we always know that there'll be lots of fun, games and laughter! This outdoor boy loves barbies on the beach, camping trips and snowboarding.

Height:
183 cm

Eyes:
Electric blue

Hair:
Sandy blonde

Best friend:
Steven

Favourite colour:
Green

Biggest talent:
Ken is great at all kinds of sports, but he's a total knockout at American football.

Top hobby:
On the weekend, Ken likes to take off. He grabs some snacks, jumps on his mountain bike and pedals off to the great outdoors!

Favourite motto:
Be the best you can be.

Ideal Christmas present:
A trendy surf T-shirt or a new pair of sunglasses.

The cause that's closest to my heart:
After diving in coral reefs last summer, Ken is passionate about protecting the ocean and all the amazing creatures that live in it.

Loves to ride his mountain bike

Water boy

Ken X

All Eyes on Steven

Steven is Ken's best buddy, but my girlfriends and I love him too! He is a smart cookie who comes out with the most hilarious one-liners. Steven gets invited to tons of parties, lighting up the room with his infectious grin.

Height:
183 cm

Eyes:
Dark brown

Hair:
Black

Best friend:
Ken

Favourite colour:
Red

Biggest talents:
Telling jokes and doing nutty impressions!

Top hobby:
Steven is a techno-whiz. He loves chillaxing with his games console or surfing the net.

Favourite motto:
Be happy!

Ideal Christmas present:
A new basketball hoop or a stack of the latest CDs.

The cause that's closest to my heart:
When he's angry about something, Steven switches on his PC. A few clicks and he's set up an on-line petition to get things changed!

Beach-time!

Always the joker!

Steven X

Barbie

and the Three Musketeers

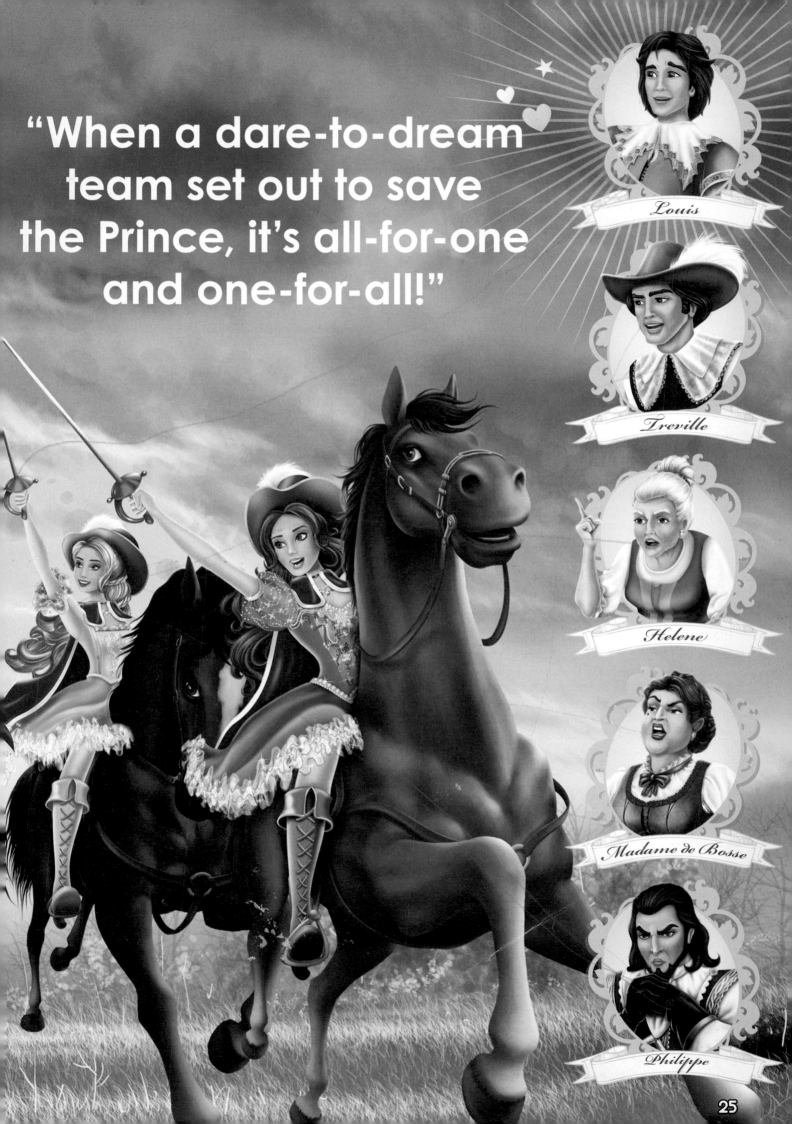

"When a dare-to-dream team set out to save the Prince, it's all-for-one and one-for-all!"

Louis

Treville

Helene

Madame de Bosse

Philippe

25

Once upon a time...

...a country girl called Corinne dreamt of travelling to Paris to become a Musketeer. Protecting the Royal Family was a great honour, but a girl had never been trusted with this task before. Corinne hoped that she might one day leave her farm and earn a place as the first female Musketeer.

When the girl turned seventeen, her mother finally agreed to let her go. Corinne's own father had been a loyal servant of the crown – now she was ready to follow in his footsteps.

"Take this letter to the Captain of the Musketeers," her mother said kindly. "I have asked Monsieur Treville to look out for you."

Corinne saddled up the farm's horse, Alexander, and got ready to say goodbye.

"Wait for me!" squeaked a little voice.

Corinne looked down to see her adorable kitten Miette running after her.

"Jump up!" smiled the girl. "We're going to Paris!" After years of waiting, Corinne's time had finally come.

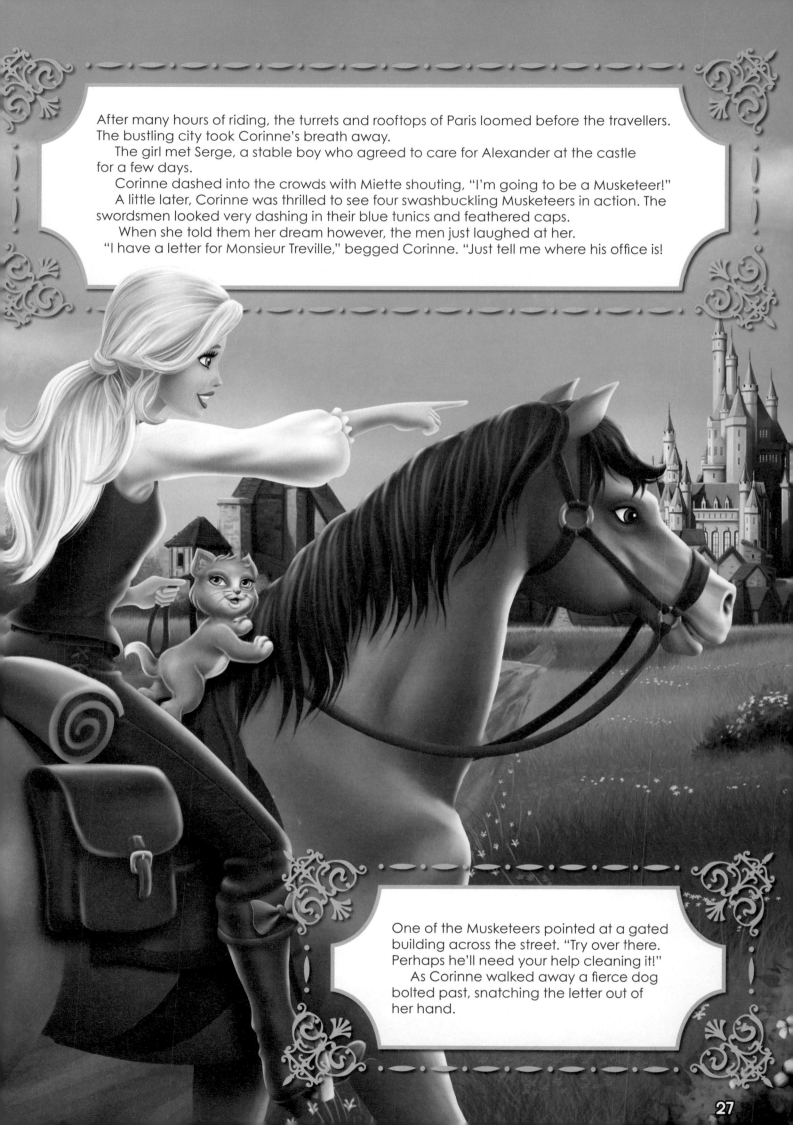

After many hours of riding, the turrets and rooftops of Paris loomed before the travellers. The bustling city took Corinne's breath away.

The girl met Serge, a stable boy who agreed to care for Alexander at the castle for a few days.

Corinne dashed into the crowds with Miette shouting, "I'm going to be a Musketeer!"

A little later, Corinne was thrilled to see four swashbuckling Musketeers in action. The swordsmen looked very dashing in their blue tunics and feathered caps.

When she told them her dream however, the men just laughed at her.

"I have a letter for Monsieur Treville," begged Corinne. "Just tell me where his office is!"

One of the Musketeers pointed at a gated building across the street. "Try over there. Perhaps he'll need your help cleaning it!"

As Corinne walked away a fierce dog bolted past, snatching the letter out of her hand.

The dog was called Brutus and he belonged to Philippe, the Regent of France. Philippe was in charge of looking after Prince Louis until he reached the age of eighteen.

Brutus took the letter and ran into a compound where Philippe was talking to Monsieur Treville. It was the Musketeers' Headquarters. Corinne chased after the hound, slipping past the Musketeer guards before leaping athletically over the gate.

"I must speak with Monsieur Treville!" she cried, standing defiantly before the two men. Philippe was very amused to meet such a daring young tomboy.

"Brutus!" he chuckled. "Give the lady her letter."

Once the Regent had swept out of the compound, Monsieur Treville lead Corinne to a seat in front of the castle.

"You knew my father D'Artagnon," she explained hopefully. "I want to be a Musketeer too." The wise gentleman nodded, but he did not have good news.

"You are not yet ready," he decided.

Corinne walked sadly away, her dream in tatters. She turned down an alleyway and suddenly Brutus was back, chasing after poor Miette.

"Come here!" cried Corinne, tearing after the kitty.

The trio raced past a fabric shop just as a beautiful girl stepped out in a shimmery pink wrap.

"Très magnifique!" cooed the stranger, noticing how her new shawl sparkled in the sunshine.

Just at that moment, Miette and Brutus stomped straight through a puddle, splattering the girl with mud.

"Sorry!" cried Corinne, running after the animals.

The stranger looked down at her ruined outfit.

"Someone arrest them!" she yelled. "It's a crime against fashion!"

Before the girl could shout any more accusations, the animals had disappeared into a rose garden.

In a quiet spot amongst the flowers, a young maid was daydreaming. The girl tossed her long golden curls, imagining that she was a guest at a fancy ball at the castle.

"A dance with me?" she pretended, stopping to sniff one of the roses. "That would be most splendid."

The girl took the arm of an invisible partner and then waltzed elegantly around the garden. Corinne winced as Miette hurtled past the dreamer with Brutus in hot pursuit.

The fearsome dog pushed his way round the maid, sending her spinning into the bushes.

"That was exceedingly rude!" shrieked the girl, her hair tangled with rose leaves.

"Excuse me!" cried Corinne.

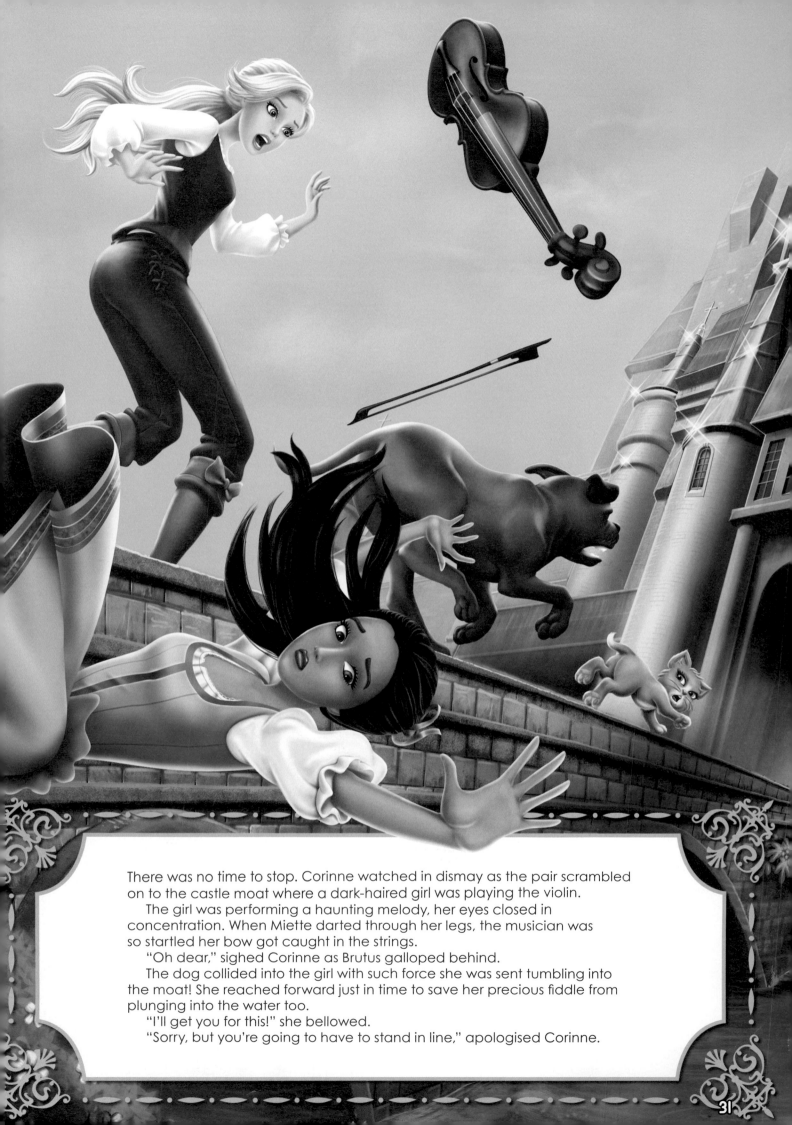

There was no time to stop. Corinne watched in dismay as the pair scrambled on to the castle moat where a dark-haired girl was playing the violin.

The girl was performing a haunting melody, her eyes closed in concentration. When Miette darted through her legs, the musician was so startled her bow got caught in the strings.

"Oh dear," sighed Corinne as Brutus galloped behind.

The dog collided into the girl with such force she was sent tumbling into the moat! She reached forward just in time to save her precious fiddle from plunging into the water too.

"I'll get you for this!" she bellowed.

"Sorry, but you're going to have to stand in line," apologised Corinne.

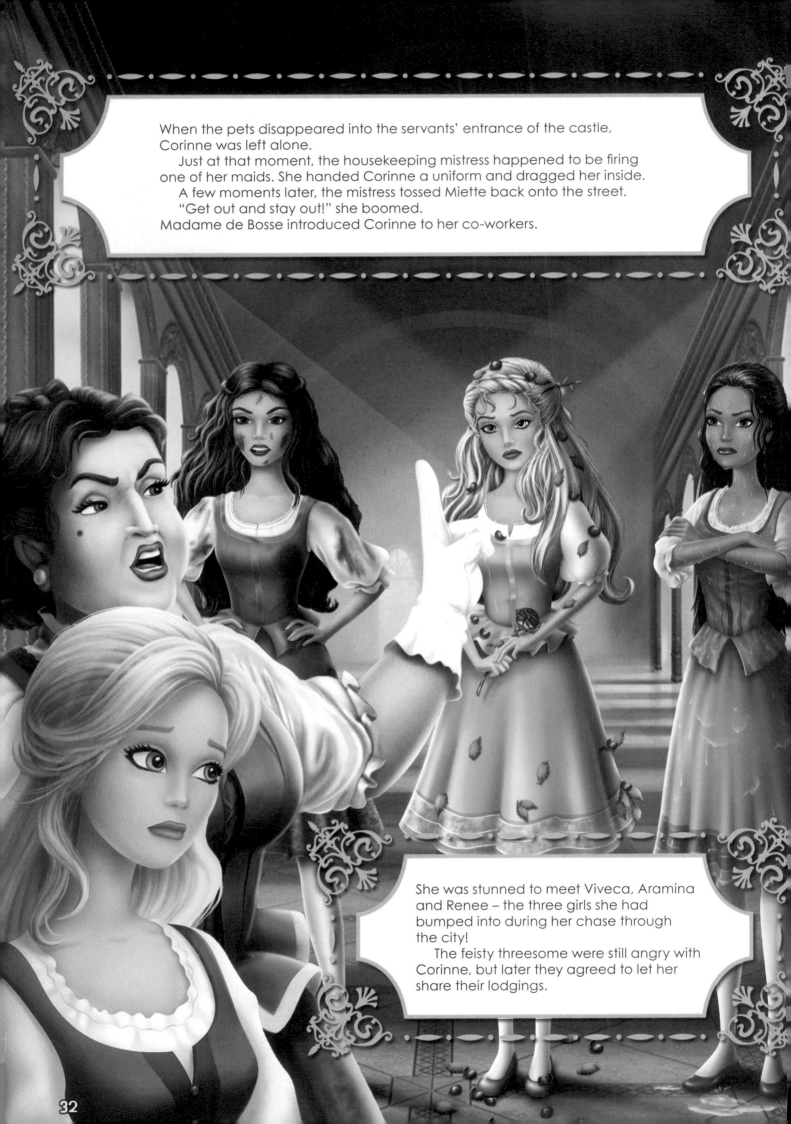

When the pets disappeared into the servants' entrance of the castle, Corinne was left alone.

Just at that moment, the housekeeping mistress happened to be firing one of her maids. She handed Corinne a uniform and dragged her inside.

A few moments later, the mistress tossed Miette back onto the street.

"Get out and stay out!" she boomed.

Madame de Bosse introduced Corinne to her co-workers.

She was stunned to meet Viveca, Aramina and Renee – the three girls she had bumped into during her chase through the city!

The feisty threesome were still angry with Corinne, but later they agreed to let her share their lodgings.

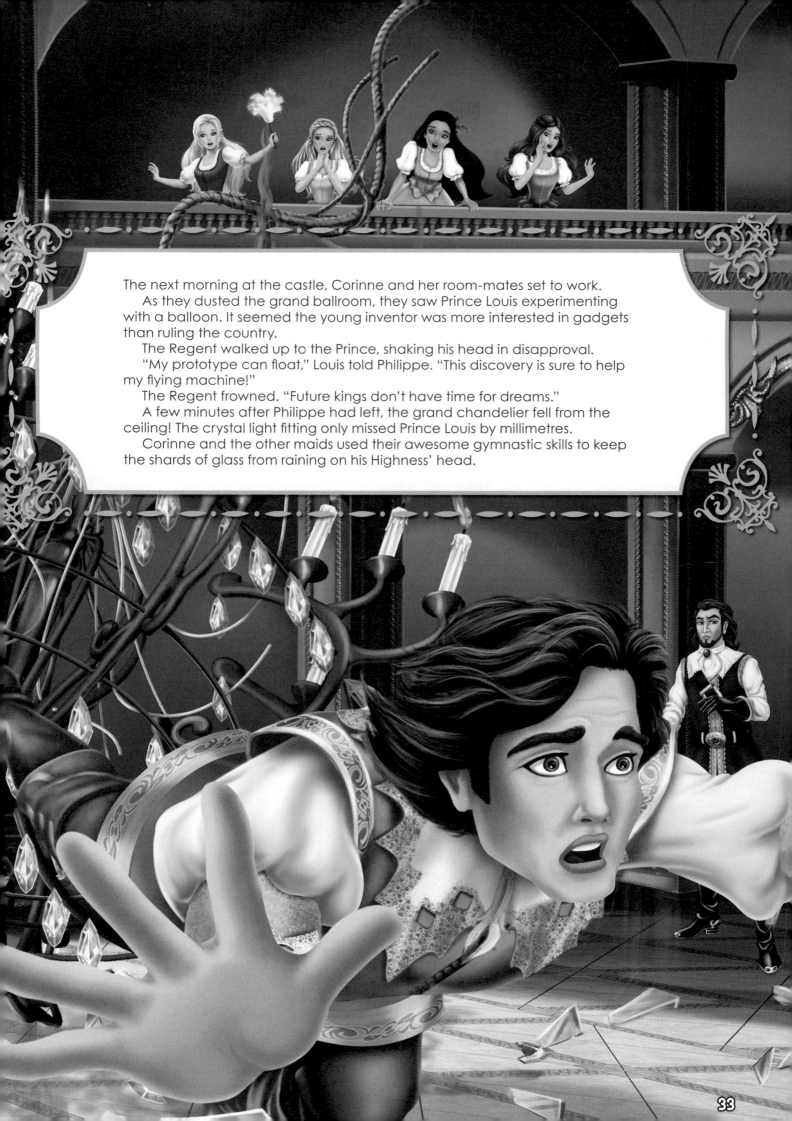

The next morning at the castle, Corinne and her room-mates set to work.

As they dusted the grand ballroom, they saw Prince Louis experimenting with a balloon. It seemed the young inventor was more interested in gadgets than ruling the country.

The Regent walked up to the Prince, shaking his head in disapproval.

"My prototype can float," Louis told Philippe. "This discovery is sure to help my flying machine!"

The Regent frowned. "Future kings don't have time for dreams."

A few minutes after Philippe had left, the grand chandelier fell from the ceiling! The crystal light fitting only missed Prince Louis by millimetres.

Corinne and the other maids used their awesome gymnastic skills to keep the shards of glass from raining on his Highness' head.

Corinne found a shiny red gem on the floor.

"Curious," she whispered, noticing that the chandelier's rope had been cut.

As the girls cleaned up the broken glass, they each revealed their dream of becoming Musketeers.

Suddenly one of the older maids called Helene hauled the foursome into a secret passageway. The girls were soon amazed to find themselves standing in an underground chamber.

"This is the old Musketeers Training Room," explained Helene. "I can teach you their fighting skills."

Corinne shared an excited look with Viveca, Aramina and Renee, then bowed before her teacher.

Helene lifted her sword. "We begin."

Corinne and her friends spent every spare hour learning how to defend themselves.

"Work together as a team," instructed Helene. "If one of you succeeds, you all succeed. If one fails, you all fail."

In Helene's day no one believed that a girl could be a Musketeer – she desperately wanted her pupils to prove those people wrong.

Upstairs in his study, the Regent sneered at his chief of staff.

"That chandelier was meant to finish the Prince off once and for all," shouted Philippe, furious that his plan had failed.

The bitter Regent believed he was much more suited to being king than his young cousin Louis. Now there were only days to go before the Prince turned eighteen. Philippe realised that he had to act now or lose his powers forever.

"There will have to be another 'accident' tomorrow," he decided.

The next day, Prince Louis was in the field behind the castle working on his flying contraption.

As he tinkered with the balloon, someone cut the rope tethering it to the ground! The Prince found himself sailing into the air, dangling by his foot.

"Someone!" he cried. "Please!"

Corinne was cleaning the windows in a nearby turret. As soon as she saw the Prince, she swung on a curtain and leapt towards the balloon.

"Hold on!" she shouted, climbing into the basket.

"Do I have any other choice?" yelled the Prince helplessly.

As the pair drifted over a forest, Corinne used all her might to avoid the trees and drag the Prince to safety.

"Thanks are in order," puffed the Prince, holding out his hand. "To whom do I owe the honour?"

Corinne did an awkward mid-air curtsey, then introduced herself.

"Since you just saved my life, why don't you call me Louis?" smiled her travelling companion.

For a little while the pair enjoyed drifting into the sunset.

"I never thought I'd see Paris from the clouds," gasped Corinne.

Louis' eyes filled with excitement. "I always knew I would."

The young Prince talked about his lifelong passion for flying, but then his face grew sad.

After the Masquerade Ball the next night he told Corinne that he would become King and there would be no more time for such dreams.

"Keep reaching for the sky," urged the maid. "Even when everyone else says it's impossible."

That evening Corinne worked at her training with renewed energy. After saving the Prince's life, she was determined to show him that she could make her dreams come true too.

As they fenced, Helene watched with true admiration. Corinne, Viveca, Aramina and Renee had finally learnt to work as a team. They were ready!

On their way home from the castle, Aramina spotted Bertram and his guards loading a wagon with heavy crates. Her friends ducked into a side street when they saw the man using a dagger to slice open one of the crates.

"That's the knife that was used to cut the chandelier," gasped Corinne, holding up the red gem, she had found after the chandelier rope had been cut.

Overhearing the Regent's plan to sneak weapons into the Masquerade Ball, the girls went to tell Monsieur Treville. With Philippe looking on, Treville searched the crates Bertram had brought in. Nothing suspicious was found.

"Stay away from the castle," warned Monsieur Treville.

Corinne and her friends were fired on the spot.

Aramina, Renee, Viveca and Corinne went home to pack their things. Instead of leaving however, Corinne convinced the girls to stay to try and foil the plot against the Prince!

"We're the only ones who know about the Regent's schemes," said Corinne. "We have a noble duty!"

Viveca started stitching four costumes while the others worked out a plan for that evening's Masquerade Ball.

Back at the castle, Philippe took his leave from Prince Louis.

"It's a shame you can't stay for the Ball," said his cousin. The Regent smiled and shook his head. As soon as he had driven out of view however, Philippe set his plot in motion.

"Return now to the back entrance," he told his driver. "We mustn't be seen."

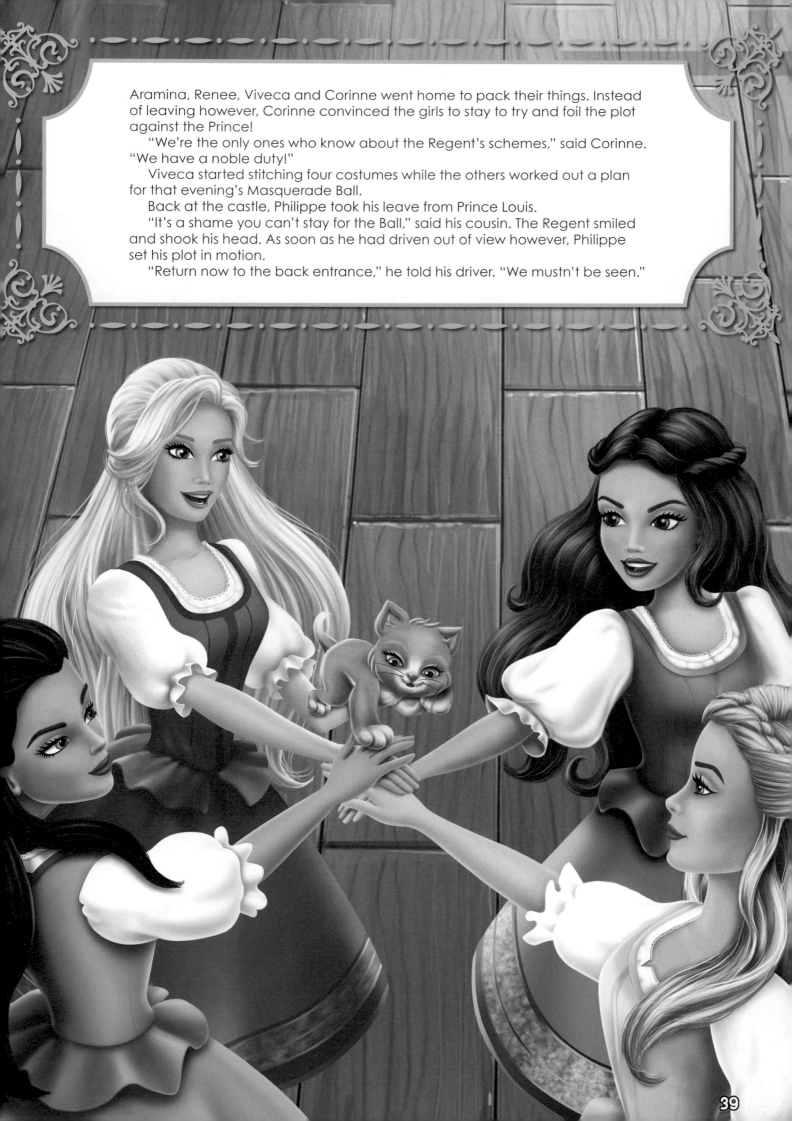

It was time for the Masquerade Ball to start. Corinne and her friends dazzled in the ball gowns that Viveca had made, hiding their faces behind exquisite masks.

"Just try to blend in," whispered Corinne, as the girls stepped into the room.

Prince Louis walked through the crowd, looking for a partner to join him in the ceremonial sword dance. Corinne gasped when he reached for her hand.

As they danced, Prince Louis was desperate to find out the identity of the mysterious beauty before him. Corinne refused to answer, scanning the room for the Regent's men.

As a cascade of fireworks exploded on the terrace, Corinne spotted the masked Philippe swooping in behind his majesty.

"Let's do this!" shouted Corinne, as she and her friends transformed their gowns into Musketeer outfits.

The guests gasped as the foursome began to fence with Philippe's men.

"All-for-one…" cried Corinne, raising her sword.

Viveca, Renee and Aramina lifted their foils to the ceiling too. "…and one-for-all!"

Guard after guard rushed at the girls, but each one held their own.

"Don't mess with the dress!" shouted Viveca, sending two hapless henchmen reeling to the floor.

Aramina flicked her fans in a dazzling display of skill.

"Shall we dance?" she asked a furious Bertram.

The duelling raged on and on, sending the ball into disarray. The battle was so fierce, nobody noticed the Prince being pulled into a secret passageway.

His plot foiled, the Regent led the Prince into one of the corridors underneath the castle. While Renee, Aramina and Viveca tackled Bertram's men, Corinne headed after Philippe. Miette even bravely took on Brutus!

"How is it that you knew about the plot against me?" asked Louis, sensing that he was in danger.

Philippe reached for his dagger, chasing the Prince up a spiral stairway.

"I should be King, not you!" he bellowed, as the Prince ran up to the castle ramparts. "There is no escape!"

Just as Philippe raised his hand to stab Prince Louis, Corinne leapt across the rooftops to block him! Fireworks filled the sky as the skilful young fencer duelled with the Regent. At last the traitor was defeated, a sword pressed against his neck.

"Arrest him!" cried Prince Louis, breathless with relief.

While Philippe was sent to prison, Louis was crowned King of France. His first decree was to thank the girls for their courage. A crowd gathered outside to hear the King's speech.

"Corinne, Viveca, Aramina and Renee," he began. "You have committed the highest acts of courage and nobility."

The friends bowed their heads so the King could touch their shoulders with his sword.

"I hereby anoint you, now and forever, as Musketeers!" announced his Majesty.

The crowd cheered and Monsieur Treville smiled. He for one would never misjudge Corinne again!

The new Musketeer felt her heart swell with pride. She raised her sword and beamed at her three dear friends.

"All-for-one and one-for-all!"

The End

Masquerade!

Have you ever been a guest at a Masquerade Ball? Covering your eyes with a pretty mask makes the atmosphere ever so exciting!

The next time it's your birthday, perhaps you could have a masquerade disco? Everyone could bring their masks, or you could all make one together at the beginning? A home-made mask will look stunning and be totally unique to you!

For each Masquerade disguise, you will need:
Tracing paper
Pencil
Empty cereal box
Scissors
PVA glue
Tissue paper
Stick-on gems, feathers and sequins to decorate
Coloured sticky tape
Drinking straw

1. Copy the mask outline from the facing page onto some tracing paper.

2. Open out an old cereal box and trace the mask shape onto the inside. Ask an adult to cut it out for you.

3. Cover the mask with PVA glue and lay tissue paper over the top. Stick at least two sheets on and then trim around the edges.

4. Hold the mask up to your face and get a grown-up to mark where the eyes should go. Your helper can then cut out a hole for each eye.

5. Now your mask is ready to decorate! Glue gems, feathers and sequins all over the mask, choosing the colours you like best.

6. When your decorations have dried in place, find a thick straw. Wrap coloured sticky tape up the entire length of the straw to make it nice and strong. Finally tape the straw to the back of the mask so that you have an elegant handle.

SAFETY WARNING
Leave the cutting to your grown-up helper, scissors are sharp!

Embellish
the Dress

Viveca has stitched the most divine layered dress for her friend to wear to the Masquerade Ball! Corinne loves the way the skirts spin and twirl as she dances, but she feels that it needs a little something extra. Can you help Viveca finish the job?

Find some felt-tip pens and then decorate Corinne's dress with jewels, bows and ribbons. You could even sprinkle on some glitter or add a sticker here and there!

Pick
a Passageway

Corinne and her friends are trying to find their way through the labyrinth of passageways underneath the Royal Castle. Prince Louis is hidden in a locked chamber somewhere in the dungeons below.

Study the secret corridors, then find the route that will lead the budding Musketeers to the key.

Chandelier

Colour Copy

Can you copy this swashbuckling picture of Corinne swinging from the chandelier in the grand entrance of the Castle? Find a pencil and then copy the contents of each square into the matching space on the grid below.

Now bring the heroine to life with all your brightest colours!

Tidy-up Time!

Teresa's bedroom has got into a terrible muddle! Can you help her tidy up by matching the pairs of lost accessories? Draw a line between the pictures so she can put each one away.

One item does not have a pair, which is it?
....

Spa Spot the Difference

When Teresa and I went to the spa for a beauty day we had a total blast! We started with a pedicure, before treating ourselves to a fab facial and make-up session.

These two photos look the same, but there are six differences in the right-hand picture. See if you can circle all of them!

Pretty
as a Picture

Sometimes getting all dressed up can be just as much fun as an evening out! Can you help me look my best tonight by finding the six words hidden in the wordsearch grid below? Look carefully – the words could be running in any direction!

H	E	M	U	F	R	E	P
E	A	R	R	I	N	G	S
W	X	N	V	F	S	Q	S
E	S	L	D	B	J	Z	R
O	G	Y	P	B	X	P	F
H	K	L	Z	G	A	M	B
S	E	S	S	A	L	G	C
L	I	P	S	T	I	C	K

Colour in the heart next to each picture clue that you find

Barbie's Shopping list

Barbie's got a whole load of retail therapy planned this afternoon! Can you work out the items on her list? Complete the words by taking letters from Barbie's name and popping them in the right spaces.

PU_S_

H___ CL_PS

SH_MPOO

P__TY D__SS

N__L POL_SH

__OOCH

Make Your Own Snowflake Wreath

I made a super paper wreath last weekend. Ever since I hung it up above my closet, my friends have been pestering me to find out where it came from! The twinkly snowflakes look ever so pretty in the evening light.

You will need:
6 used kitchen towel rolls
Pencil
Scissors
White poster paint
Paint brush
Newspaper
Wire coathanger
Sheets of silver paper
PVA glue
Glitter

1. Take a used kitchen roll and mark it with a pencil in three equal sections. Carefully cut the roll where you've marked, so that you make three mini-tubes.

2. Repeat this with all the kitchen rolls until you have 18 sections in total. Now cut slits halfway up each of the sections on both sides.

3. Use poster paint to coat all the rolls, then lay them on some old newspaper to dry.

4. Ask an adult to bend the coathanger into a circle shape, with the hook positioned at the top. Slot your tubes onto the circle frame until the wire is completely covered.

5. Take a square of paper at least 15 cm wide and fold it in half and then half again. Fold the square one more time across the diagonal to make a triangle. Hold the point of the triangle in your hands and then snip shapes into the paper. Unfold the paper to reveal your unique snowflake!

6. Repeat step five until you have a little stack of snowflakes ready to glue onto your wreath. Lay the snowflakes onto some newspaper, then dot them with PVA glue. Sprinkle some glitter over them, then shake the excess away.

7. Carefully stick your snowflakes onto the tube circle until the entire wreath is covered.

SAFETY WARNING
This ice-cool make-it requires some cutting. Ask a grown-up to help you with all the stages that use scissors!

Step back and enjoy your own piece of frosty magic! The snowflake wreath will look totally enchanting hanging from your bedroom door this winter.

Why not…?

♥ **Experiment with different coloured snowflakes**

♥ **Tie ribbons at intervals around the wreath**

♥ **Add some stick-on gems to the decoration?**

Lovely
in Lilac

My sparkly gown was just the thing for the Annual Snowflake Ball! The guests were driven across the snow in glittering silver carriages. It was such a magical experience.

Can you colour me in using your prettiest pencils or felt-tips?

Ten Ways

to keep the Chills at Bay

Winter is such a magical time of year. Cold, bleak days never get me down – there's too much to do both inside and out! Here are my top tips for making the most of the chilly season.

1. Go for a frosty morning walk
Pull on a hat and dig out your toastiest mittens! Walking on an icy morning really does blow the cobwebs away. Look out for icicles, robin redbreasts and holly bushes with scarlet berries.

2. Bake a batch of muffins
I don't know many people who don't adore muffins! Ask an adult help you make a dozen, experimenting with different flavours. Your house will soon be filled with the most delicious, warm smell. Mmmm!

3. Have a pyjama day
When it's really bitter outside, it's time to get cosy. Dig out your dressing gown and slippers then curl up in front of the fire with a DVD or your favourite magazine.

4. Organise an ice-skating trip
Ice-skating is a tricky skill to master, but practising is a whole lot of fun! Lots of temporary skating rinks are set up at this time of year. Get a group together and arrange a visit soon. Don't forget your camera!

5. Star in a home movie
If you're spending the day at home, why not use the time to get creative? Write a script then ask your family or friends to help you make a film of it. Think of all the fun you could have with costumes, make-up and the sets!

6. Have a snowball fight
It doesn't snow very often, so when it does get out there and have a great time! No one can resist a playful snowball fight – the more friends you can rope in the merrier.

7. Make a winter mural
Collect pine cones, leaves, stones and moss from the garden or park, then see what you can make with them. Arrange your finds on a large piece of card then add drawings and a sprinkle of glitter.

8. Invite your friends round for hot chocolate
Hot chocolate is the scrummiest drink in the world. Before your friends arrive make sure you've got loads of milk in the fridge, plus cream, sprinkles and mini-marshmallows to put on top!

9. Go to the library
Libraries truly are amazing places. You can lose yourself in a faraway adventure just by browsing through the bookshelves. Some libraries even hold special storytime sessions and activities in the school holidays.

10. Have a hot indoor picnic
Lay down a rug, then spread out a front room feast! Hotdogs, pizza slices and potato wedges all taste nicer when eaten with your fingers! Why not also try mugs of hot soup with crusty bread rolls dipped in.

Pathways
to Piper

Piper can be a mischief sometimes! The little Westie has jumped out of my school bag and scampered down the street. Put a big tick next to the path that will lead my friends and I to the cheeky pup.

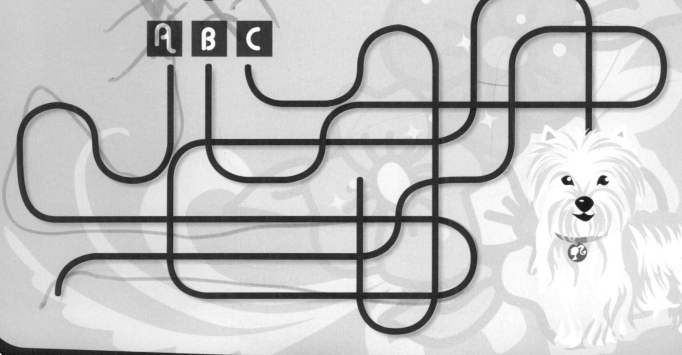

Dotty Disguises

Which one of Corinne's friends also dreams of becoming a Mus-cat-eer? Join up the dots to reveal her brave comrade's true identity and colour them in!

Paris People

The brave girls in 'Barbie and the Three Musketeers' were the original action heroines! The French foursome were determined to follow their dreams no matter what obstacles were thrown in their way.

Unjumble the letters below then write each of the characters' names in the spaces underneath.

1. **NAMARAI**

_ _ _ _ _ _ _

2. **RINCENO**

_ _ _ _ _ _ _

3. **ENEER**

_ _ _ _ _

4. **SATTIR**

_ _ _ _ _ _

Make a Cuddly Carry Case

When I go to a sleepover at Nikki or Teresa's, I always like to pack my favourite cuddly toy. My pink teddy is old now, but I still love him to bits! Instead of squeezing him in my overnight bag, I've made a special house for him to travel in.

Why not make a carry case for your favourite soft toy? All you need is an old cardboard box and a few craft supplies. Stand the box upright and then paint it all over in a bright shade. When it's dry, cut a hole at the front for a door and some windows at the sides.

Now you're ready to start decorating! The next steps are completely up to you. Here are a few ideas to get you started:

♥ Write your toy's name in bright letters above the door.

♥ Stick some wrapping paper inside to make a pretty carpet.

♥ Trim your box with cotton wool, feathers or stickers.

♥ Draw flowers around the walls.

♥ Put rows of stick-on gems round the window frames.

Be as creative as you like! After all, Very Important Teddies deserve the best treatment!

Catwalk Mix·up

Nikki, Teresa and I are getting ready for a fund-raising charity show! Put this photo of us in the correct sequence then find the hidden word to complete the phrase below.

d   s   e   r   s

Let's ♡♡♡♡♡ up!

Frock
Exchange

I always recycle my clothes! When I'm done with an item I take it to my local vintage store and swap it for something new. I've tried five gorgeous pieces on today, but I really can't take them all home with me. Can you choose the two that would suit me best? Colour in the heart next to your favourites.

Pink t-shirt

Pink pleated dress

Pink belted shimmer skirt

Cerise feather dress

Pale pink bow smock

Fashion Show
Finder

My pre-show nerves never last very long. Once I step onto the catwalk and the camera bulbs flash I start strutting to the beat and enjoying myself! Study the picture carefully and see if you can answer all the questions dotted across the pages. Colour in each heart every time you complete a task.

What colour is Nikki's dress?

Point to the girl wearing diamond hoop earrings.

How many flowers are there on the backdrop?

The Prettiest Party Cake!

Are you having a party anytime soon? Here's a quick recipe for a fairytale treat that would look perfection on any top table! Why not try to make one the next time you invite some friends for tea?

You will need:
2 shop-bought layered Angel Cakes
284ml tub of double cream
1 pot of vanilla yoghurt
Washed and chopped strawberries
Washed and chopped raspberries
Chocolate chips

1. Take the Angel Cakes out of their packets and carefully pull apart each of their three layers. Place the bottom third of both cakes next to each other so that they form a pink square.

2. Pour the double cream into a bowl and then ask a grown-up to mix it with an electric whisk until it starts to firm up a little. Gently fold in the vanilla yoghurt with a spoon.

3. Spread a third of the cream mixture onto the base of the cakes, then arrange a few strawberries and raspberries on top.

4. Lay the next two white sponge layers onto the fruit and spread with the cream mixture. Repeat the layering until the yellow top of the cake is decorated with the remaining cream and fruit.

5. Take a handful of chocolate chips and sprinkle them over the cake – heaven!

Barbie™

Love
Letters

This heart-shaped word grid holds the name of one of Barbie's most precious pet's. Cross out all the letters that are printed more than once and you'll be left with the six that spell out the pet's identity.

Q	G	G					C	N	P
P	H	T	J	I	C	I	S	M	
K	C	V	I	Z	D	H	C	K	
L	Q	F	U	C	B	W	R	J	
	R	B	D	R	U	P	M		
	E	V	L	A	O	R	S		
		G	F	Z	X	G			
		O	J	Y	M	F			
		C	X	V					
		B							

Barbie adores
_ _ _ _ _ _

67

Secret
Storybook

My friends and I adore fairy stories! When Teresa and Nikki come for tea, we spend hours making up stories of our own, each more fantastic than the last.

Would you like to write your own storybook? All you need to get started is a pretty pen, the page opposite and a stapler.

How to make your Secret Storybook:

♥ Ask a grown-up to remove the page opposite from the annual.

♥ Cut the page in half along the middle dotted line, then fold each piece of paper in half again. Slip the pages inside each other, using the number to help you get things in the right order.

♥ Staple the book through the middle to hold the pages in place.

After you've written your story add some pictures and pretty decorations.

7

The End

My very own
Barbie™
Storybook

Written and illustrated by

. . . .

3

4

Once upon a time,

1

6

5

2

Odd Picture Out

An odd-one-out is hiding in each of these groups of pictures. Can you find it every time? Colour in the heart as you finish each puzzle.

Mika ♡   Mika ♡

Mika ♡

Mika ♡

♡ Tiara

♡ Tiara

♡ Tiara

♡ Tiara

Ballet Shoes ♡

Ballet Shoes ♡

Ballet Shoes ♡

Ballet Shoes ♡

71

Colour
Co·ordinated!

I was over the moon when a gold-edged envelope slipped through my letterbox the other day. It was an invitation to an award ceremony in the city! Can you help me put together the right outfit for the evening? Colour in the heart next to the items that you think I should wear.

Barbie™

Thumbelina

"Let me tell you a story that proves even the smallest person can make a big difference..."

In a beautiful field, hidden amid the trees and flowers lived the Twillerbees

– tiny people no larger than your hand. One of the Twillerbees was called Thumbelina. She wasn't a bit shy. In fact she was incredibly brave. One day she summoned her best friends Chrysella and Janessa to show them the wings she'd made to help them fly.

Thumbelina soared away over the flowers. Below her was the Twillerbaby patch, a circle of precious blooms holding the next generation of Twillerbees. Her friends joined her in the air, but their fun soon came to a halt. Humans were approaching!

Inside one of the cars, a girl called Makena was talking on her mobile to her friend Violet, while her parents discussed their plans for the field. Desperate to outdo her spoilt friend, Makena asked her father to transport Thumbelina's flowerbed to her room.

A little later, Thumbelina, Chrysella and Janessa crept out of the tulip petals. They were stunned to find themselves in Makena's bedroom! After managing to escape from her hungry dog, Poofles, they hid in a doll's house. Finally Makena, still on the phone to Violet, strolled into the room.

The friends were tiptoeing away when they overheard Makena's conversation. "My parents are destroying the whole field for their new factory," she boasted. Thumbelina flew angrily back inside shouting, "I'm not going to let you ruin my home!"

Makena tried to grab the tiny girl, but Thumbelina managed to escape again. When she was free and reunited with her friends however, she had second thoughts. "I have to go back," she told Janessa and Chrysella. "You go and delay the workers – I'll stay here and find some way to stop them for good."

Back inside Thumbelina told Makena all about the Twillerbee world. She offered to help the girl impress Violet by growing plants and weaving them into cool handbags, if Makena would persuade her parents to abandon their plans. She set one condition – Makena must tell no one about her tiny accomplice.

Back at the field Janessa, Chrysella and the other Twillerbees were making sure demolition couldn't begin. First they used all their magic powers to grow gigantic weeds which bound and tethered the diggers and trucks to the spot!

Next the tiny girls conjured enormous vines and ordered them to undo the bolts holding the machines together. When the crew tried to start the diggers they broke apart. Myron the foreman phoned Makena's father to tell him that they'd lost at least a day's work!

Meanwhile Violet was visiting Makena. She scoffed when she saw the gorgeous 'designer' bag that Thumbelina had secretly crafted. Humiliated, Makena decided to go back on her promise. "Tomorrow I'll show you something that no other human has seen," she bragged to Violet.

Next morning in a half-hearted attempt to keep to her side of the bargain, Makena tried to speak to her parents about shelving their construction project. As usual they were too busy to listen to her. "There, I tried," pouted Makena, trudging sadly out of the room.

Thumbelina, riding on Poofles, went in search of Makena. She spotted a picture of a family dining in a beautiful garden. Finding Makena outside, the girl explained that her dad had once promised that when her parents made their fortune they'd have a place like that to sit and have tea.

Back at the site, things were going from bad to worse for the builders. Janessa painted a scary face on the head of a sunflower and grew it to a fearsome size. Meanwhile Lola organised birds to bombard the workers with acorns.

In the apartment, Makena decided to give Thumbelina a makeover. The tiny girl admitted she'd never had one. Her friends spent their time laughing, playing and talking. "We Twillerbees take our friendships very seriously," Thumbelina explained.

Thumbelina told Makena that she considered her a friend. She led the girl outside and showed her the special makeover that she had done for her – Makena's roof terrace was now in full bloom. Touched, Makena tried to cancel Violet's visit, but it was too late.

Just at that moment Violet burst onto the terrace. "Where's 'the most unique thing we've ever seen' then?" she sniped. Thumbelina, who'd hidden herself in a tree at the sound of voices, realised that Makena had betrayed her. Devastated and angry, she returned home.

Thinking back to Thumbelina's words about friendship, Makena finally understood that Violet was anything but her friend. She jumped on her bike and pedalled to the field. "You're my friend, Thumbelina!" she cried, searching the flowers. "I'll still save this field, I promise."

Hearing such honest words, Thumbelina appeared. The two friends decided to work together to save the field before the Twillerbabies were born. Back at Makena's home, the pair set about creating the idyllic garden of her parents' dreams in the empty greenhouse on their roof terrace.

When Makena showed the garden to her parents' they were overwhelmed, yet still they refused to consider halting construction. "To you it's just a little field, but to me it's my whole world," interrupted Thumbelina. Finally listening, Makena's family had minutes to drive to the field in time to save the Twillerbees.

Forced to cycle when their car hit traffic, Makena pedalled furiously to reach the field. Her heart raced as she remembered that the Twillerbuds were due to open that very day. Although she was just one girl, she knew that she had to stop Myron and his workers.

Makena arrived to find Myron bearing down on the Twillerbuds. Bravely she confronted him. "You're just a kid," he bellowed. It was a big mistake! Thumbelina and her friends flicked the controls and the digger lifted Myron up in its jaws. At that moment Makena's parents arrived. "The project's off!" they both yelled.

When the builders had gone, Makena's parents thanked Thumbelina for creating their dream garden. "We thought it could be a place where we have time to talk to each other," said Makena. "From now on, we promise we will," said her mother. Thumbelina smiled as the stunning Twillerbuds began to open up before them.

Twillerbee
Pictures

Twillerbees really are the most enchanting little creatures you could ever hope to find in your garden! At the weekend Stacie and I were having an arts and crafts session when we discovered a new way of making cute Twillerbee pictures.

Have a go! The chalk really does create a magical effect.

You will need:
Black card
Pencil
Tracing paper
Silver pen
Red chalk
Pink glitter pen

1. Put a sheet of tracing paper over the picture of Thumbelina on the page opposite and trace her outline with a pencil.

2. Transfer the picture onto a sheet of thin black card, then go over the pencil outline in silver pen.

3. Use a stick of chalk to very carefully draw round Thumbelina's silver shape, taking care not to go over the lines.

4. Very gently smudge the chalk outwards using the edge of your finger so that you create a pink glow all around the Twillerbee.

5. Finish off your picture by shading inside with the pink chalk and then drawing the details in Thumbelina's face and clothes using a glittery pink pen.

What a fluttery flowery cutie pie! If you want to, why not cut out petals from coloured paper and stick some blooms next to Thumbelina too?

Flower Count

Twillerbees have a unique power – they can make plants grow at super speed! I think that Thumbelina and her friends must have tiptoed into my garden because all the flowers have grown to twice their normal size.

My favourites are the gorgeous pink ones. Can you count up how many I've got growing in my garden today?

There are 11 pink flowers

Cute

I've decided to take some of my flowers over to Summer's house, it's going to be a such lovely surprise for her! Make my picture look pretty by filling the page with colour. The key below will help you choose the right shades.

Colour·by·Numbers

Colour key

| 1 | 2 | 3 | 4 | 5 | 6 | 7 | 8 | 9 | 10 | 11 |

Fun with friends

Thumbelina loves to giggle and play with her friends Chrysella and Janessa! The tiny Twillerbees' favourite times are spent flying round the garden with their beautiful petal wings.

Can you spot six differences between these two pictures? Colour in a flower for every one that you find.

Let's Go Outside!

Teresa and I are wrapping up to take Taffy out for a walk in the countryside. An outing in the fresh air always blows the cobwebs away!

Have you done something active today? Here's a list of my top ten outdoor hobbies. Tick the ones that you like to do too.

1. **Walking in the countryside** ♡
2. **Ice-skating** ♡
3. **Running with the wind in my air** ♡
4. **Cycling as fast as I can** ♡
5. **Hula-hooping in the garden** ♡
6. **Packing picnics with friends** ♡
7. **Scootering through the park** ♡
8. **Making camps in the woods** ♡
9. **Playing hide and seek** ♡
10. **Joining in a football match** ♡

Totally Into You!

Now that you've heard about me, I'd love to read about you! Can you find a pretty pen and then answer the interview questions below?

Name :

....

Age :

....

Birthday :

....

Height :

....

Eyes :

....

Hair :

....

Pets :

....

Best friend :

....

Favourite colour :

....

Biggest talent :

....

Top hobby :

....

....

Favourite motto :

....

Ideal Christmas present :

....

The cause that's closest to my heart :

....

Can I have your autograph? Write your name in here :

....

Fill the photo frame with a drawing of yourself doing the thing you love best!

My Special Friend

PEACE, LOVE, LIPGLOSS

ANCIENT MYSTERI

MY FAVORITE THIN

GIRL POWER

Kiss and Make·up

Raquelle's make-up always looks so fresh and natural – no wonder designers want her to model their clothes.

Here are my pretty pal's tips on getting your cosmetics just right for that special occasion.

♥ Keep it natural!
Beauty really does come from the inside out. Don't cover up your lovely features with layers of foundation, eye shadow or blusher. Just use a touch on special occasions.

♥ Ask an adult to help you
Your mum, auntie or grown-up sister have probably been wearing make-up for years. Before a party, why not ask them to give you a makeover, sharing their beauty tips as they work?

♥ Got to gloss
Lipgloss is much lighter than lipstick and it gives your mouth a lovely sheen. Look for shades in fruity flavours and your pout will smell nice too!

♥ Pinch then puff!
To find the best place to put blusher squeeze your cheeks. Apply a tiny dab of rouge to the area that naturally flushes.

♥ Shoulder shimmer
A little bronzer or glittery powder dusted over your shoulders and neck will give you a healthy glow.

♥ Be allergy aware
If a product stings or brings you out in a rash, don't use it any more. Look out for cosmetics that say 'hypoallergenic' on the label.

♥ Cleanse, tone and moisturise
Before you go to bed, squeeze a little cleanser into a cotton wool ball then gently wipe it over your face everytime you've been wearing make-up. A touch of toner and moisturiser will keep your skin in tiptop shape!

Let's Dance

Wanna make up a cool dance routine with your friends? Crank up the music and get ready to boogie!

Cut out the dance cards on the facing page then ask your friends to give them a shuffle. Pick a card from the top and follow the move, then go on to the next one. Work your way through the pack until you've stepped out a complete routine!

When you're ready for a new tune, just shuffle and start again.

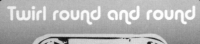

Twirl round and round

Reach for the sky

Sidestep to the right

Wiggle the hips

Jump into a star

Look left and right

94

Sway to the music
Barbie

Sidestep to the left
Barbie

Wiggle your fingers out in front
Barbie

Wave your arms in the air
Barbie

Spin on the spot
Barbie

Take three steps back
Barbie

Twist and jive
Barbie

Kick your legs out to the left
Barbie

Cross your arms over your chest
Barbie

Point your finger to the audience
Barbie

Take three steps forward
Barbie

Shimmy left and right
Barbie

Touch your left knee with your right elbow
Barbie

Sink to the ground
Barbie

Touch your right knee with your left elbow
Barbie

Do the locomotion
Barbie

Kick your legs out to the right
Barbie

Click your fingers to the beat
Barbie

Ask an adult to help you with the cutting!

Mirror
Messages

I got a surprise when I looked into my dressing room mirror this evening, Raquelle had written me a message in red lipstick! She used the special back-to-front code that we write when we want to keep something extra-secret.

Help me decipher Raquelle's message. We'll need to hurry, I've got to leave for Nikki's birthday party in ten minutes! Use the code cracker below to decode each letter in the phrase, then write it in the space below.

Code Cracker

A=Z	H=S	O=L	V=E
B=Y	I=R	P=K	W=D
C=X	J=Q	Q=J	X=C
D=W	K=P	R=I	Y=B
E=V	L=O	S=H	Z=A
F=U	M=N	T=G	
G=T	N=M	U=F	

What do you think we bought for Nikki's birthday? Join the dots to find out!

8
7
6
5
1
2
3
4

Txt Talk

Teresa and I spend at least one evening a week at each other's houses – talking clothes and sharing girly gossip! We love to text messages to our friends and make plans for the weekend.

Can you spot how many mobile phones are hidden in this picture? You'll need to look very carefully!

There are ♡ missing mobiles

Perfection
in Pink

I don't know what gown to wear this evening to the Pretty in Pink Ball! Will you be my stylist? Colour in the heart next to the outfit that you think will look the most glamorous on the dance floor.

Pink layered dress

One shoulder sheath dress

Dark pink gown

Full skirted dress

Pale pink dress

Let's Talk Shopping

Nikki and Raquelle were thrilled when they bumped into each other at the mall the other day! Can you work out what the friends are saying? Look at each picture clue and then write in the right letters to complete the speech bubbles.

Hi there _ _ _ _ _ _ _ _! I've just had my _ _ _ _ _ done. What's in the _ _ _?

Hi _ _ _ _ _ _, how are you? I've bought myself a pair of shiny new _ _ _ _ _. Shall we _ _ _ _ _ Barbie and see if she fancies a drink and a slice of _ _ _ _ at the diner?

jigsaw
Jumble

This snap of Teresa and I is one of my favourites – it was taken on a blustery Sunday afternoon stroll! Can you help fill in the blanks by drawing a line between each jigsaw shape and the right space in the photo?

Cool Clothes Quiz

The clothes we like can say a lot about our personalities. Are you a cute tomboy or a head-turning trendsetter?

Take my special fashion quiz, then add up your answers at the end. It's time to find your style…

1. You've arranged to meet your friends at the mall. Do you…
a. Jump with joy, counting the minutes- until it's time to go. ♡
b. Spend hours in front of the mirror, working out what to wear. ♡
c. Pull on a sweat top and go for a run first. ♡
d. Make a list of things that you'd really like to look out for. ♡

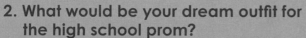

2. **What would be your dream outfit for the high school prom?**
   a. An up-to-the-minute gown, just like the ones in your fashion magazine. ♥
   b. A dramatic number that will get all eyes on you. ♥
   c. Nothing too dressy – you don't want to look like a meringue! ♥
   d. Something elegant, feminine and pink. ♥

3. **What's your favourite accessory?**
   a. Statement handbags. ♥
   b. Glittering jewels, bangles and earrings. ♥
   c. Clips to keep your hair out of your face. ♥
   d. Shoes – you can't get enough of them! ♥

4. **What do you put on when it's raining outside?**
   a. Funky patent boots for stepping in puddles. ♥
   b. You don't go out – rain is the enemy of couture clothes. ♥
   c. An outdoor jacket and hiking boots. ♥
   d. A cute belted mac with a bright print. ♥

5. **What's best – skirts or trousers?**
   a. Trousers at the mo, but that might change next week. ♥
   b. Skirts that show off my funky tights and must-have shoes. ♥
   c. Trousers – they're so much easier to do stuff in! ♥
   d. Skirts cos they're girly, twirly and fun! ♥

Mostly a's
Funky Fashionista
You and Nikki would make great shopping partners! You are devoted follower of fashion, keeping up-to-date with all the latest looks in the high street. It's hard work but worth it, you always look fantastic!

Mostly b's
Dramatic Dresser
When you go out, you like people to notice! You and Raquelle love eye-catching statement clothes that put you both firmly in the centre of attention. You adore bold colours, and anything that sparkles.

Mostly c's
Outdoor Girl
Sounds like you're a tomboy, just like Summer. You're a fresh-faced outdoors person who's far too busy to worry about clothes! Your natural style suits you perfectly.

Mostly d's
Pretty in Pink
You adore feminine, individual clothes, just like me! We like to ring the changes and try all sorts of styles, although we can't resist popping on a little bit of pink whenever we get the chance.

Best Friends Forever

Nikki, Teresa and of course you... mean everything to me! Will you add your self-portrait into the happy scene below? Draw yourself in next to Teresa to make the gang complete!

Gorgeous Gift Tags

Christmas makes my tummy jump with excitement. It's such a glittery, snowflake-sprinkled time, full of presents, parties and festive fun!

When you're wrapping your presents this year, try making your own gift tags to top off each one. All you have to do is copy or trace the designs below onto some thin white card and then get decorating! When you're finished, use a hole punch to push out a circle in each tag and then thread a short piece of ribbon through. The result will be truly enchanting, I promise!

Dancing Dictionary

Let Your Heart Dance Every Day

When I put on my ballet shoes, my heart really does skip with pleasure! How many words of three letters or more can you spell out of the phrase above? Challenge a friend or family member to a race and see who can come up with the most in two minutes!

....

....

....

....

....

....

....

....

Winter
Wishes

Thank you so much for reading my wonderful, wintery annual! I've dreamed up a skyful of happy wishes for the year ahead, which one would you like the best?

Colour in the snowflake next to your favourite wish, then think about it when you wake up each icy morning. Keep wishing until Spring and it just might come true!

A surprise party

Brand new shoes

A shimmery new dress

Hand-knitted mittens

A day out in the snow

A pet to play with

Ice-skating with friends

A trip to the zoo

Answers

Page 47
Pick a Passageway

Page 52
Pretty as a Picture

H	E	M	U	F	R	E	P
E	A	R	R	I	N	G	S
W	X	N	V	F	S	Q	S
E	S	L	D	B	J	Z	R
O	G	Y	P	B	X	P	F
H	K	L	Z	G	A	M	B
S	E	S	S	A	L	G	C
L	I	P	S	T	I	C	K

Page 50
Tidy-up Time!

Teresa's **powder blue clutchbag** doesn't have a matching pair.

Page 51
Spa Spot the Difference

Page 53
Barbie's Shopping List

PURSE
HAIRCLIPS
SHAMPOO
PARTY DRESS
NAIL POLISH
BROOCH

Page 58
Pathway to Piper

The correct path is **A**.

Page 59
Dotty Disguises

It's **Miette**.

Page 60
Paris People

1. ARAMINA
2. CORINNE
3. RENEE
4. TRISTA

Page 62
Catwalk Mix-up

Let's **dress** up!

Page 64
Fashion Finder

Nikki's dress is **blue**.
Teresa is wearing diamond hoop earrings.
There are **3** flowers on the backdrop.
Nikki is wearing a diamond belt.
There are **15** overhead spotlights.
The runway carpet has a **flowery** pattern.
There are **10** cameras.
Barbie has a brooch pinned to her dress.

Page 67
Love Letters

Barbie adores **TAWNEY.**

Page 71
Odd Picture Out

Mika ♡   Mika ♡   Mika ♡   Mika ♥

♡ Tiara   ♥ Tiara   ♡ Tiara   ♡ Tiara

Ballet Shoes ♡   Ballet Shoes ♡   Ballet Shoes ♥   Ballet Shoes ♡

Page 88
Flower Count

There are **12** pink flowers.

Page 90
Fun with Friends

Page 96
Mirror Messages

DON'T FORGET TO BRING NIKKI'S BIRTHDAY PRESENT!
Barbie and friends bought Nikki some **perfume.**

Page 98
Txt Talk

There are **6** missing mobiles.

Page 100
Lets Talk Shopping

Hi **Raquelle!** I've just had my **nails** done.
What's in the bag?

Hi **Nikki**, how are you? I've bought myself a pair of shiny new **shoes**. Shall we **phone** Barbie and see if she fancies a drink and a slice of **cake** at the diner?

Page 101
Jigsaw Jumble

Page 106
Dancing Dictionary

There are dozens of word that fit the bill, here are just a selection:

**Novelty / Hour / Cuddle / Letter / Cord
Teeny / Lottery / Cloud / Teeth / Thorn**

How many did you come up with?